Know what? You're in a vicious cycle

When you feel low, you tend to stop doing things. You don't go out so much, you avoid seeing friends and you even stop listening to music or watching sport.

As a result, you feel even lower, and then you feel like doing even less. It can seem such a relief to cut down and withdraw. It's tempting to take to bed, or sit or lie around all day. But if you do, you end up all seized up, feeling stiff, tired and overwhelmed.

It's like: the less you do, the worse you feel, the worse you feel, the less you do. And it keeps going round and round and round...

Things can get quite vicious.

So,what's going on?

1 **Symptoms make things hard.**
Low, not sleeping/tired.
Scared, fed up.
Can't be bothered.

4 **Count the cost.**
Feel worse, lose confidence.
Less pleasure, less
achievement, see friends less.
You feel worse and worse.

2 **Struggle to do things.**
Everything seems harder/more effort.
Things seem pointless/not enjoyed.
Going through the motions.

3 **Cut down/avoid things
that seem too hard.**
Do less and less.
Only do things you must/
should do.
"You" time squeezed out.

Turn over to break the cycle

DO YOU KNOW WHAT YOU JUST DID?

You broke the cycle

All it took was a little bit of positive action - turning that page in this case.
Now all you have to do is take another tiny step, then another and another.
What steps? That's what this book is about – to show you the easy steps you can take to break that cycle into bits and start feeling better.
It involves making choices. Choosing to do things that make you feel better, rather than hiding away feeling worse and worse.

Important question coming up

WHAT DOES YOUR DAY LOOK LIKE?

When things seem hard, it's easy to lose your previous routine. It's tempting to lie in bed longer, stay up later, or have a longer nap each afternoon. But before you know it you lose the pattern and structure of your day.

What times do you typically get up?

… and go to bed?

These are the anchors that start and end your day. Other anchors that split your day are mealtimes. So, when do you eat?

Breakfast

Lunch

Tea/dinner

Around these points are all the other activities of the day. Meeting friends, household chores and more.
You need to get a routine going again. And start building in activities that you know are good for you.

First, look at what you do just now

Think about yesterday

Start by thinking about the last 24 hours. Write down everything you have done. Include things like getting dressed, talking to a friend on the phone, washing your hair, etc. Then score them out of ten for pleasure, achievement and feeling close to other people. The first few spaces are filled in to show you how to do it.

Doing this will help you understand what's good in your life and also to realise what's missing.

About closeness

Feeling close to others is really important, but when we're down, we sometimes hide away. If your diary doesn't have enough things with a good closeness score, this book will help you sort that out.

	Pleasure	Achievement	Closeness
Talking to Alison on the phone.	9	3	10
Cleaning my room.	1	10	0

Pleasure	Achievement	Closeness
☐	☐	☐
☐	☐	☐
☐	☐	☐
☐	☐	☐
☐	☐	☐
☐	☐	☐
☐	☐	☐
☐	☐	☐
☐	☐	☐
☐	☐	☐
☐	☐	☐
☐	☐	☐
☐	☐	☐
☐	☐	☐
☐	☐	☐
☐	☐	☐

Check your list and pick out the things you did that scored highly for pleasure, achievement or closeness to others. Write them down here.

ANYTHING MISSING FROM YOUR DAY?

What about things you've stopped doing?

Your day might not have contained all the things you like to do, so have a look through the list below and tick the one's that apply to you. Things you used to enjoy but haven't felt like doing lately.

Enjoying sport. ☐

Seeing your friends. ☐

Listening to music. ☐

Watching a film. ☐

Pursuing a hobby. ☐

Watching TV. ☐

Phoning or texting friends. ☐

Gardening/looking after plants. ☐

Going for a walk/Getting some fresh air. ☐

Doing exercise. ☐

Going to a class or club. ☐

Playing a musical instrument. ☐

Reading a good book, magazine or blog. ☐

Practicing relaxation techniques. ☐

Doing drama. ☐

Going to church, mosque, temple or synagogue. ☐

Spending time with family. ☐

Cooking or baking for pleasure. ☐

Helping other people. ☐

Well ticked!

Now choose an activity you want to do

USE WHAT YOU'VE FOUND TO START FILLING YOUR DAY WITH GOOD STUFF

Remember, the things that make you smile.

One of the reasons we feel worse when we stop doing things, is the fact that it's usually the things we like that we avoid first.
No wonder life seems to go down and down!

To start it going up again, you need to pick good things to fill your day with. Not all the time – just one thing to start with. So the next step of your plan is to look at the lists you just made and pick one of the things on them.

Pick something that used to give you pleasure, or a sense of achievement. Or something that you think is worthwhile or made you feel close to others.

Just one thing to start with.

An activity you value and see as important to your life.

NOW WRITE IT HERE SO YOU DON'T FORGET IT.

_____

_____

_____

_____

GOOD

You've just written down the thing you're going to start doing again. Something worth getting up for.

Now, you're going to do it

NOW PLAN WHEN YOU'LL DO IT

Say what and when

Think about the activity you want to do first.

Write down *what* you will do, and *when* you will do it into the Activity Planner on the next two pages.

Just now it will stand out as the only activity there.

Go, ahead, write it in.

You don't want it to feel lonely, so soon you'll be adding other activities into the Activity Planner.

But to start with just include:
*   The single activity you planned - the one you wrote down on page 15.
*   Next, add your daily anchors: the meals you have through the day, and the times you get up and go to bed.

There's plenty of time to add more activities, but for now just focus on the first activity you're going to do.

My activity planner

Plan a balance of activities over the days and week.

Get into a routine- a time to get up, eat, go to bed, and do the household chores, or perhaps to go for a walk, meet friends or attend a regular class.

Choose things you Value and give a sense of Pleasure, Achievement or Closeness.

Plan in the key essentials that otherwise will build up and cause you problems- paying bills, cutting the lawn, doing the washing up, ironing, having a hair cut etc.

The plan is to build what you do up over a few weeks so you end up with one activity planned in each part of the day. Leave some gaps for the unexpected things that crop up. Have some time just for you.

linked
worksheet
www.llttf.com

	Morning	Afternoon	Evening
Monday			
Tuesday			
Wednesday			
Thursday			
Friday			
Saturday			
Sunday			

Now build on it

REMEMBER THAT LONELY ACTIVITY?

Now let's give it some friends

Add some more regular activities

Having to get out of bed to walk the dog or feed the baby can be a real pain, especially on cold mornings, but it's also a great way to feel better. No dog? No baby? Then make yourself a routine with other things. Shaving and showering. Cleaning the house. Popping to the corner shop to say hello and buy some bacon and eggs. Cooking them for breakfast! Can't get out? Make the most of activities you can do.

And if you rebuild your routine with things that involve others (ringing your mum each morning, walking with a friend every Wednesday) you'll feel even better because of that closeness thing we mentioned before.

It needs to be a daily routine, too. Choose something every single day that you need to get up and out of bed for. Don't lie in - remember, the less you do the worse you feel, the worse you feel, the less you do. Add these to your Activity Planner.

More good stuff on the next page

ADD SOME MORE OF THE GOOD STUFF

Plan a series of other activities, then add them one by one into your Activity Planner. Make each activity small and not scary. Don't be ambitious, be easy on yourself. And don't worry if you have to keep crossing things out, there's plenty of space.

- Choose some of the good stuff that helps how you feel.

- Add in some of the things you've cut down or stopped doing that used to be good too.

- Choose things you value and give a sense of pleasure, achievement or closeness.

- Build things up over a few weeks so you end up with one activity planned in each part of the day.

With each activity you add, you're breaking that vicious cycle, and making it spin the other way so you feel better and better.

Are you ignoring important things?

Some activities may seem hard or boring. Paying the bills, looking after yourself, keeping up with the housework - they can all seem too much trouble when you're feeling down.

The problem is some activities are necessary, and if you don't do them it makes you feel worse and can get you in a mess. So here's what to do: choose one thing that wasn't in your diary but should have been, and plan to do it - now.

Pay that bill. Make that call. Get your hair done. Do some tidying. Wash the dishes.

You'll feel loads better afterwards and you'll be able to add it to your diary and put a 10 in the 'achievement' box!

Aim for the following

You know what makes you feel good.

Across each day and week you need to get a mix of activities that help.

Start with the activities you can change most easily.
Aim for variety so you address each of the key areas:

1. Pleasure: things that make you feel good.
2. Achievement: things you value and see as important.
3. Closeness: where you connect with important others.
4. Finally don't forget to do things that are important and necessary.

Each of these activities breaks the vicious cycle and makes you feel better.
But don't rush. Some activities need to be built up to slowly.

TAKING STEPS THAT MOVE YOU FORWARDS

Some activities may be good for you, but seem just too hard to do all at once. You need to work up to doing them step by step.

How?

Have a look at the example opposite.

For example

Jack used to like meeting his friends for a walk in the park, but since he's been low, he hasn't had the energy for it. This is what he wrote in his plan for getting back to meeting them.

Step 1. Go to the park and just sit there enjoying the peace and quiet.

Step 2. Go back to the park and walk by myself. Don't need to talk to anyone if I don't feel like it.

Step 3. Get into the habit of walking by myself 2 or 3 times a week.

Step 4. Get in touch with one friend and arrange to have a walk and a chat.

Step 5. Go to the park with my friend at a time when we're likely to see the others.

Step 6. Arrange to meet the others next time they're walking in the park.

Step 7. Keep going – get into a routine and feel the difference!

Jack knew he could take one step a day, or one step a week, it didn't matter. What mattered was having a plan and making steady progress towards getting some fun back in his life.

Right, that's enough of Jack. Now back to your plan.

WRITE DOWN AN ACTIVITY THAT YOU NEED TO BUILD UP TO STEP BY STEP HERE

_____

_____

Now think about the little steps you can take towards doing it. Don't be overly ambitious, be easy on yourself. And don't worry if you have to keep crossing things out, there's plenty of space.

1. I'm going to _____

2. Then I'm going to _____

3. Next, I'm going to _____

4. Then I'm going to _____

5. _____

6. _____

7. _____

8. _____

9. _____

10. _____

SOUNDS EASY DOESN'T IT?

But you know change sometimes isn't that easy

Remember all those failed New Year's resolutions? Promises to change that seem hard? Or maybe we forget, or find we can't be bothered, or talk ourselves out of things?

So, let's recognise something. It's hard to make changes. That's why we've asked you to pick activities to do that you know can be good for you.

But if you find you get stuck doing a particular activity, here's a helping hand to make a plan to do it that will work.

Turn over to make your plan.

Make a plan!

Planner Sheet

1. What am I going to do?

2. When am I going to do it?

3. What problems or difficulties could arise, and how can I overcome them?

Is my planned task -

Q. Useful for understanding or changing how I am?

Yes **No**

Q. Specific, so that I will know when I have done it?

Yes **No**

Q. Realistic, practical and achievable?

Yes **No**

HOW
DID
IT GO?

Life's all about learning

If you make a plan and everything goes smoothly- that's great!

But you can also learn a lot from when things go wrong too. So, if there are problems with your plan- that's great too. It's great because you can play detective and learn.
So, if you got stuck, or something was difficult, ask yourself some questions. Was the problem something *internal* – inside you, or *external* – for example a problem caused by someone else, the weather, or unexpected circumstances?
Use whatever you discover to make your next plan even better.

You'll find a useful Review sheet to help you with this learning on the next two pages.
Try to get into a sequence of *Plan* (using the Planner sheet), *Do*, and *Review* (using the Review sheet) for whenever you are planning more difficult activities. That way you will keep moving forwards.

How did it go?

Review Sheet

What did you plan to do? Write it here:

If yes:

1. What went well?

2. What didn't go so well?

3. What have you learned from what happened?

4. How are you going to apply what you have learned?

Review Day

Did you try to do it?

Yes **No**

If no: what stopped you?

Internal things (forgot, not enough time, put it off, didn't think I could do it, couldn't see the point etc.).

External things (other people, work or home issues etc.).

How could you have planned to tackle these things?

WHAT IF SOMETHING GOT IN YOUR WAY?

Learn from it. So as soon as you've written your next plan, think about what could stop it happening. Are there things that might trip you up? What about other people? Could someone be unhelpful at any stage?

When you've figured out what could block your progress, work out another mini-plan for getting around the obstacle. It's called unblocking.

Things to watch out for

Don't try and make every change possible all at once.

Be realistic – you're planning for success not a let-down. You know your own personality and how inpatient or ambitious you are. That's where it's important to be wise and plan just one main change a day to start with.

So, pick just a few things to get you started, and make a separate plan to do each using the Planner sheet. Then plan them in across the day and the week using the Activity Planner.

1. Leave some gaps for the unexpected things that crop up.
2. Include some time just for you.
3. Remember the anchors - a time to get up, eat, go to bed.
4. Add in some more routines like a regular time to do the household chores, or perhaps to go for a walk, meet friends or attend a regular class.
5. Make sure your plan fits with your values/ideals of how you want to live.

But don't forget that some things are important to do even if they aren't much fun or seem difficult.

AT THE END OF EACH DAY

Use your Happy List to help you remember

Each evening, sit down and write down three things that you:

- Have enjoyed.
- Felt was a job well done.
- Or helped you feel close to someone else.

After a few days, you'll have a list of great things that you can look back on. It will help you remember how you're changing things.

Time to give yourself a pat on the back!

WHERE TO GET EVEN MORE HELP

Sometimes it can seem too difficult to start getting going again, even with small steps. That's when you need a bit more help than this little book can give.

You can get it at the Living Life to the Full course **www.llttf.com**

It's free and the number one site for low mood and anxiety recommended by NHS Trusts and teams in England.* It's packed with ways to lift your mood and start living a happier and healthier life.

There are links on there so you can connect with other people who are making changes to their lives too.

*Bennion et al, 2017. BMJ Open http://bmjopen.bmj.com/content/7/1/e014844